The Raystede Handbook of Homoeopathic Remedies for Animals

Proceeds from the sale of this book will be devoted to the homoeopathic work at Raystede

The Raystede Handbook of Homoeopathic Remedies for Animals

Index by
Maurice Prior

A story by M. Raymonde-Hawkins, MBE,
in collaboration with George Macleod, MRCVS, DVSM,
telling the value of homoeopathic treatment as practised
in The Raystede Centre for Animal Welfare, Ringmer,
East Sussex, England.

SAFFRON WALDEN
THE C.W. DANIEL COMPANY LIMITED

First published in Great Britain in 1985 by
The C.W. Daniel Company Limited
1 Church Path, Saffron Walden,
Essex, England.

ISBN 0 85207 167 1

Printed in Great Britain by The White Crescent Press, Luton, Beds.

PREFACE

As a worker for the welfare of animals over most of my life and as a result of my experience in the value of homoeopathic remedies from childhood (when a tumble was always accompanied by a scream for **Arnica**), I have long yearned for the opportunity to share the virtues of homoeopathic treatment with others. With increasing focus on animals during the years I have very naturally wished that these simple and harmless remedies should be used more extensively rather than the orthodox drugs too many of which have side-effects. I therefore launch this family handbook as a story covering many animals and many illnesses hoping that its simplicity will enable many who are now on the fringe of alternate medicines to explore further and experience the marvellous values of Homoeopathy.

M. Raymonde-Hawkins, Raystede, September 1985

CONTENTS

INTRODUCTION

The original intention in introducing this little book was to write the story of a normal family with its usual domestic pets and discuss the various accidents and illnesses that occurred to them. To tell the recommended homoeopathic treatment successfully used in every problem, physical or mental, that besets animals during their lives in the average home. It was intended, therefore, to make this book into a story that would appeal to, and interest, the young equally as the more mature animal owner. The story was to include the family moving into a house where a diminutive, starving, unweaned kitten was found in the garden needing immediate attention. This was to be the opening to a series of family pets, the dog, the pony, the goldfish, rabbit, budgerigar and goat, but, the ominous brass plate on the next door "semi-detached" had already frightened the youngest member of the family who ardently believed that brass plates only indicated the presence of dentists! More than little persuasion was needed to induce him to get help for this nearly dead kitten from the tall Scot next door, whose name appeared on the brass plate followed by the mysterious letters M.R.C.V.S., A.F.Hom. The child gradually accepted the explanation that the neighbour was a Doctor for Animals, although he did not realise the implications of the A.F.Hom, which, of course, indicated that it was a very special Homoeopathic Veterinary Surgeon.

Being at the age when his enquiring mind was developing he was prone to ask innumerable questions, and, once his shyness was overcome the veterinary surgeon next door was no longer a remote and rather awesome man. On the contrary it was not long before he became our little boy's hero and was plied with simple but intelligent questions whenever there was an opportunity to speak over the garden fence or to make an excuse to take the kitten into the surgery for treatment for some real or imaginary ailment.

He offered to help in the surgery! And no greater joy was his than when allowed to put instruments into the sterilizer, to clear up the surgery floor or table, although he needed to stand on a chair to reach instruments from the shelves of the clinically sparkling cabinets. While doing so, many questions poured out, such as "what does A.F.Hom. mean?" and wisely Uncle George, as he had now become, skipped over explanations of A for Associate and F for Faculty and endeavoured to concentrate on this rather clumsy word HOMOEO-PATHY, which, he explained, put into simple English, really meant LIKE WITH LIKE.

"Like! what?" came the natural query, but this problem, as helpfully as possible, was cleared up in his mind by the explanation that once upon a time a very clever doctor named Hahnemann discovered that by treating his patients with the juices or compressed parts of various plants and certain metals he had noticeable results when swallowed by humans. He could, by searching very carefully, select plants or metals that gave pains or high or low temperatures similar to the pains or high or low temperatures from which Dr. Hahnemann's patients were suffering.

This was all very puzzling to our young friend and so simpler tactics of explaining "Like with Like" were adopted. For instance, supposing that it was a very very cold day outside and a very heavy snow and his feet were very very cold in his boots. If he took his boots off and put his feet into a hot water foot bath they would warm up in a very short time, but, as soon as his boots were on again his feet would become as cold as before. But if he now walked in the cold snow his feet very quickly would become warm and remain warm so that was **cold** feet cured by **cold** snow or "Like with Like".

On a very hot day the eating of ice-cream or drinking of cold drinks would not really cool him down as successfully as drinking one hot cup of tea, a **hot** body and a **hot** drink, again, "Like with Like".

FOREWORD

Dr. Hahnemann and many other doctor friends followed, extremely carefully, all the details of what certain plants and parts of plants could do in curing illnesses. Over the years of skilled research every experiment carefully carried out convinced them more and more that they could find a "matching" plant or metal, that is a every experiment carefully carried out convinced them more and more that not only could they find a "matching" plant or metal, that is a "like" plant or metal to match every illness. They also found that usually a very tiny dose was able to cure more readily than if a massive dose was given which would probably cause trouble or greater illness. For instance, our young friend has been taught that certain berries on the shrubs in his garden were poisonous and that under no circumstance must he ever pick them or eat them. Either they would make him very ill, or he might even die. Yet now he learns from Uncle George that a tiny speck of that very same shrub treated, reduced, compressed and shaken into alcohol to a very minute amount, and again reduced and again shaken, or "sucussed" as the Doctor called it, could cure a disease and make the patient quite well; so long as the Doctor had selected the **like** poison to cure the **like**, or similar illness.

How puzzling! Yes, and even now after a hundred years no Doctors have really discovered it sufficiently to be able really to explain why a berry diluted so much by shaking and diluted again is, nevertheless, so powerfully present that taking small doses can be so effective. Our young friend remained puzzled (his name by the way is Peter) and only gradually began to understand the elementary facts of the power of homoeopathic treatment until his kitten, now growing into adolescence, and becoming as inquisitive as his owner, got itself into dire trouble by exploring the farm across the road. It came home soaking wet and with obviously a very bad cold, eyes running and sneezing and certainly unable to take any nourishment and not really well enough to move. How quickly he was rushed in to Uncle George for the help of "homelyopathy" as Peter called it, not too unwisely did he give it this name, for once these remedies have been carefully studied, much help for illnesses can be given from the "home", from the "homely" medicine chest and the quick and inexpensive tablets or granules can be administered the moment the trouble is spotted. Often they can be given with success, or at least with much help before the veterinary surgeon needs to be contacted, or while he is awaited.

School holidays provided ample time for Peter to spend in the surgery and to glean more and more of the importance and value of homoeopathy, as well as how to sterilize the instruments. Also to learn a great deal about the very special handling and storage that is necessary for the various homoeopathic remedies which can be prepared for animals in various forms. For some animals the little tablets create no problem: they are sweet to the taste and dogs will usually accept them as "sweets". However, when dealing with a suspicious dog that has been given unpleasant medicines on previous occasions it is useful to have the remedy in powder form. This then can be tipped into the side of the mouth, or, if that is not easily done, sprinkled onto a spoonful of tempting food or milk.

Cats, properly handled, can be given a tablet by merely opening the mouth in the correct way. Pop the tablet at the back of the tongue, then, hold the mouth closed and stroke the throat to assist the passage of the tablet downwards. Of course, powder may prove an easier way of administering, even to a cat, but we know one cat who demands it hidden in double cream!

Homoeopathic tablets and all homoeopathic medicine should be treated with great respect. Storage is important and should preferably be in a dark container, also they must be stored away from bright light or heat and must never be kept near perfumes or strong smells like carbolic or peppermint. The remedies should never be handled but transferred from the container into the cap and then from the cap, tipped into the mouth. Handling should be avoided whenever possible. To humans it is recommended to crush the tablets between the teeth, never swallow them in water but, to ensure the animal taking it properly when there is no chance of it being chewed first, then it must be tipped onto the tongue.

The dose should be given to the animal half an hour before or after a meal and never with a bulk of food. During a course of treatment it is essential to stick to the homoeopathic remedy and not introduce any other medicines like laxatives or treatment of an orthodox nature.

To our young friend all animals brought into the surgery provided great interest and he listened with rapt attention to the advice and instructions given to the patient. He also watched directions being painstakingly written on the package which contained the powders or tablets, and he learnt how often they were to be taken and all the golden rules that are so familiar to those who have practised homoeopathy over the years. He learnt that very acute or severe conditions must be given one dose every 15 minutes for one hour and then followed by one dose every 2 hours until success commenced. If the animal had a problem that was not urgent but giving constant pain, then the customary prescription was one tablet three times or twice a day for four days and easing off as improvement set in. If the animal came into the surgery with a trouble that was already some months old then possibly the remedy would be for a set period of say three days and then report results, because homoeopathically there would rarely be an absolute repetition of the former dosage. Either the number of hours between each dose would be altered or the potency would be changed and possibly a suitable or appropriate remedy substituted for the next three days.

Homoeopathic remedies sometimes act very slowly and good results are often found to be developing long after the treatment has been given. It is very necessary to be patient and watch very carefully any symptoms that arise or that disappear soon after the remedies have been administered.

The story was to cover 15 years of animal ownership for a growing family but why instead have we had to deal with many more animals and many more problems than would fit into one family? The simple answer is that we would hope no **one** family would have **all** the problems that we hope to discuss in this book!

During these pages we wish to point out not only the usefulness of homoeopathic treatment but also how the remedies themselves work. It is of much importance too that the animal owner should value the virtues of homoeopathy by realising that the Homoeopathic Veterinary Surgeon or Doctor does not always deal directly with the symptom but approaches the whole animal and its characteristics. Perhaps this introduction will help both the young and old reader to realise that this is not only the family's safe way to health, it is also the way to avoid undesirable drugs with the side-effects that so many types of modern medicines induce in pets as well as themselves.

Let us therefore, instead of staying in the confines of the family home during these pages, take the pets commonly handled in the family and, hopefully, the professional and life experience of a Homoeopathic veterinary surgeon (very humbly supplemented by the lay experience of an animal welfarer). Let us put into the hands of animal owners the simple and safe way to give help to minor problems down the lifetime of the four-footer in every family, always, of course, calling for the support of the professional surgeon as the need arises and even his surgical work can be greatly helped by the support of homoeopathic remedies both before and after an operation. Let us, therefore, eavesdrop in the surgery of the Homoeopathic veterinarian and listen to the various problems that are brought in from day to day by people with animals such as we ourselves are all handling in our daily lives.

The veterinary surgeon has only his and the owner's observations on which to base any diagnosis when the animal is presented to him. The human patient is able to express in words his symptoms and can give a good guiding picture of his problems by describing his sensations, discomfort and pain and, of course, indicate its location. The animal can give no such clues to the veterinarian.

Examining the animal, taking its temperature and looking for any perceptible signs of accident are all that is available to the observer except that, and this is the important factor in the Homoeopath's detailed study of his patient, he regards the "personality" of his patient. All living creatures, whether on four legs or two, consist of three "parts". The physical body which of itself has no capacity for sensation except through the second "part" which is our own "self", that is our own "personality" or, as Hahnemann calls it, the "Vital Force" which is "us", just **individually** and only "we ourselves" unlike any other human being. Without our body and without our brain it is as a "force" a separate entity. It is our and the animal's third component, thus enabling all creatures to use their physical bodies by the dictates of knowledge gained through the brain which is, in itself, influenced by that third "Vital Force" which is "individuality", our own individual "personality". And so too we know that no two cats are alike, no two dogs, no two horses have identical personalities but all have brain or mental capacity. All have physically similar storage bodies which store functionary parts, livers, hearts, lungs etc. It is the "Vital Force" that animates the material body in each and every creature, it rules the body and keeps it in one whole harmonious and healthy condition whenever it has the opportunity, and, when pollution and the individual does not interfere.

In order to realise the personality of an animal, a veterinary surgeon can often gain more indication of its personality (its type), by observing it in the waiting room or in its own home or by studying its behaviour on the surgery floor before it reaches his table. Some owners can help by giving symptoms that have caused them to come for help. But their explanations are not always helpful and an experienced Homoeopathic veterinary surgeon can observe the animal and gauge its type by meeting it and discerning its characteristics, thereby gaining, in advance of any physical examination on his table, the drug picture that it represents in its personality. It is that "personality" which he, with his perception will proceed to treat.

EAVESDROPPING IN A SURGERY OF CANINE PROBLEMS

So to dogs. The first patient comes in with the age old problem of EAR TROUBLE and the story is: "My dog has been shaking his head and now he is scratching his ear and making it bleed. He is holding his head on one side, indicating that he is in great discomfort, if not pain". Help is sought from the veterinary surgeon, who with the use of his auriscope quickly detects a condition of Ear Canker. Here in Homoeopathy there are four remedies that cover most of the acute cases; **Hepar Sulph.**30c, **Merc.Sol.**6c,**Tellurium** 6c and **Arsenic.Alb.**6c. If the condition has been continuing for a long time and the owner has not troubled to bring the dog previously to a veterinary surgeon then a longer course of **Merc.Corr.** or **Rhus Tox.** may be necessary. There may, of course, be yet another problem, mites in the ear or bruising as a result of an accident, but the frequent cases are overcome quite easily by one or other of these remedies. In the case of mites the particular remedy that he will recommend is **Sulphur** 6c.

The next dog that is brought in is a bouncing, slightly mad young Alsatian. The owner is completely weary of its boisterous behaviour, lack of discipline and the fact that it is chewing up nearly everything and everybody. The owner is in despair and is contemplating parting with the animal because she cannot cope with its nerves and constant barking, apart from the fact that occasionally it is becoming aggressive to the children and visitors. The dog is loved to a certain extent but the human owners are developing a fear of it because, although only young, it shows aggressive tendencies. In diagnosis, immediately, in the young dog, one's mind goes to teething and the veterinary surgeon points out to the owner that the dog is young, needs a lot of exercise and activity and suitable toys to exercise its gums on, so that its teeth can come through more easily. He also suggests doses of **Calcarea Carbonica** and **Chamomilla**. For the hysterical condition there are answers homoeopathically. The purely excitable puppy can probably be reduced to much more sensible behaviour by one or two doses of **Belladonna** or **Magnesium Phosphate**. Where it is a slightly older animal that is frightened of noises, such as on Bonfire Night, or the sudden noise of the exhaust of a car, then a suggestion of **Phosphorous** or **Borax** comes to mind. The number of excitable dogs that cause their owners problems, whether they are fighting dogs or chewing dogs or even car sick dogs, is considerable and too many of the animal welfare societies have to receive them into their care, too often for the last sleep. Dogs are so readily discarded with one or other of these problems, whereas if it is a human baby, trouble is taken to deal with the very problems for which the dog has to be discarded. A little homoeopathic treatment for car sickness can be readily available with **Cocculus,** and there are very few of these simple problems in the young dog that cannot be overcome with good exercise, good food, plenty of toys to chew and an affectionate firm friendship between animal and owner.

A frequent reason for coming into the veterinary surgeon's surgery with a doggy problem is because of skin trouble. Skin troubles always take a long time to cure but our experience has repeatedly been that the orthodox treatment can fail where homoeopathy has repeatedly proved to be successful. A case in point was a curly coated black Retriever that had been under orthodox treatment for three years. The veterinary surgeon explained to the owner that he had scraped the bottom of the barrel for help for her dog and there was nothing left but to have the dog put to sleep. In desperation she came for help, homoeopathic help, and joyfully within six weeks the coat was beginning to grow and has continued ever since following treatment with **Psorinium** and **Arsenic Alb.** Other cases involved the use of remedies such as **Merc. Corr., Thallium, Selenium** and **Petroleum.**

Homoeopathy invariably treats the **"type"** apart from treating the **symptom** of the animal, and the prim little Dachshund with its short coat, sleek movement and tidy mind, is treated completely differently from the shaggy old sheep dog who does not really seem to worry when his coat is matted and that he is dishevelled and untidy. One Alsatian that we have had was a very typical example of the tidy dog calling for **Arsenic.Alb.,** to cure its tendencies to be afraid, in various potencies in its homoeopathic treatment. It even ate from one side of the plate until there was a straight line down the middle before it started on the second half. With its toys it regularly piled them up when the game was finished and put them in one corner of the field or one corner of the room, never resting until all were tidy. That dog had a specially tidy mind and was accordingly treated as one would expect of that type of person. The nervous dogs are ones that need very special and patient treatment.

For the dog that is frightened of noises, frightened on Bonfire Night or frightened of movement, there are remedies that are invaluable and we have an example of a very shy St. Bernard dog that was so terrified in a thunderstorm that the owners discarded it at the beginning of the summer, dreading going through another season of anxiety with him. He came into the hands of a Friend of Raystede at our Raystede Centre for Animal Welfare at Ringmer and that summer the homoeopathic tablets which were consecutively administered, **Phosphorus** and **Borax**, so quietened that dog he was prepared to walk around the garden during the wildest of thunderstorms. Travel sickness too is another problem with some dogs. They are discarded very often because the owners have to spend a lot of time in the car, they like to have their dogs with them, but the dog is miserable. A dose of **Cocculus** before the journey helps to calm down and prevent sickness. Simple problems such as worms in an animal should not be treated until it is certain that there are worms present in the dog's motion and when one is quite sure that it has worms, then these can be treated quite successfully with remedies such as **Filix Mas.** The vicious dog is very often the product of inter-breeding or of ill-treatment but it is not impossible to overcome even this. In many cases the animal is only biting out of fear or self-protection. We have a case of a dog that has been ill-treated by children, that will bark quite crossly when he sees them but would not now think of snapping at them as a result of correct homoeopathic treatment.

The simple homely problems can usually thus be overcome by kindly care, good food, regular exercise and a homoeopathic canine pack always kept handy. When a cold starts, **Aconite** can be administered and very often distemper or hard-pad or parvo-virus (which entails great expense in injections which are not always successful) is eliminated by the simple administration of harmless homoeopathic remedies such as **Arsenic.Alb.** or **Phosphorus.**

Some animals will not readily take even the tiny homoeopathic tablets but they can be dissolved in milk or administered in powder or granule form. They can, of course, be emptied into the side of the dog's mouth and there is much less difficulty in administering homoeopathic medicines than some of the larger pills that the inexperienced owner finds difficulty in somewhat clumsily "pushing down" the throat.

Homoeopathic remedies too are inexpensive and do not incur frequent visits to the veterinary surgeon which so often worries the animal as well as the bank balance of the owner!

There are more problematical things like hip dysplasia which can be coped with if seen early enough before changes have occurred or the joint destroyed. Whenever surgery is needed, such as in speying or neutering operations or some severe amputation, then homoeopathy plays its important part: **Arnica** administered before and after, followed by remedies like **Bellis Per,** and **Staphysagria.**2 Problems of loose tummies following a change of diet or a period of being left alone will often create fear in a dog which produces diarrhoea. Here a very valuable remedy is called in known as **Podophyllum**, others include **Carbo.Veg.** and **Arsenic.Alb.** and equally for constipation there are the tried and trusty remedies of **Nux Vom.** and **Carbo. Veg.**, also **Opium,** but the diet must always be watched, as well as exercise, because administering medicines is not necessarily the primary way of keeping an animal fit. The remedies only have to be administered when something has gone wrong in the dog's life, either physically or mentally and then it can be helped considerably.

The next patient was a sorry little Jack Russell, usually the terror of his road and normally the dominant dog of the area. Despite his dainty build he usually won all his battles but two successive fights had left him in much discomfort. The first fight had turned a wound into a septic abscess and the pain was obvious, but the second fight, which caused him to be brought in for professional help, had left him with jagged open bites and his assailant, a Bulldog, who was quite determined to teach him a lesson not to fight, had also left bruises.

The veterinary surgeon applied immediate first aid with **Arnica** soaked pads (dilution 1-10) to the bruises. To the open bites similar soaked pads were applied with **Hypericum** in the same proportion. For the painful abscess following hot fomentations, three days doses of **Silicea** 30 were provided. The pain of the abscess removed, then **Arnica** 6 was administered by mouth and all was well within a week, as well as much respect for the Bulldog down the road. The Bulldog himself was too fat and had signs of heart trouble and as a result of the fight, it was recommended that his food should be considerably decreased and **Crataegus** 6 was administered for three days.

During this consultation, excitable barks and high pitched puppy yelps could be heard from the waiting room. That was the next patient and the distraught owner could not put up with the constant destruction of everything in the house which was caused by this puppy (of very uncertain parentage) for he had chewed up everything, carpets, cushions, table legs, everything his little aching mouth could clench with his painful gums became victim of his destruction. His hysterical barking was causing trouble with elderly neighbours and the puppy now was to be discarded. No veterinary surgeon likes to destroy an animal when he knows the condition is not chronic and that a little patience and time will relieve the owner of worry. In this case the puppy left the surgery with a relieved owner carrying two envelopes containing **Chamomilla** for teething and **Magnesium Phosphate** for the excitability. Three weeks later a happier owner expressed her pleasure and said that she would not part with the little dog for anything. Such reports and results are so satisfying.

The Greyhound that followed came only halfway into the surgery and sat down to have a long scratch. This was checked by the owner who lifted him to the surgery table where he proceeded to ignore the veterinary surgeon and the owner and just scratched! There was little need for the owner to say why he sought help, it was obvious that the eczema condition of the skin was the cause of the trouble. In order to discover more about its condition there were certain questions put by the veterinary surgeon. "Did this dog seek cool places in which to lie or warm places and prefer to be near the fire?" He examined the sores to see if they were weeping and showing secondary infection or whether there were patches of sticky pus or whether the skin was encrusted. Accordingly various remedies would have been recommended, the one in this case was **Psorinum** but it could have been, with the varying temperament of a dog or the varying appearance of the skin, either **Petroleum** or **Merc. Corr.** or **Graphites.** The decision lying entirely upon the various patches that were causing the trouble.

The fascinating little Pug that followed appeared to be sensibly managed and to behave kindly to his companion which was a snuffling old Pekinese. Both had need of help. Although being well fed and groomed they did not give the appearance of good health. The Pug soon demonstrated why he was brought, for he started skating on his bottom on the surgery floor, indicating that he needed immediate help for his anal glands. He had showed unwillingness to go upstairs for several days which suggested discomfort in the rear and was now frequently biting under his tail. The secretion had impacted and there was inflammation in his glands and the tenderness could soon have developed into a serious abscess. **Hepar Sulph.** 30c for three days was the successful remedy but **Silicea** 30 would have been necessary if the condition had been chronic. Where the glands have opened already and are discharging pus then **Calcium Sulph.**6c would have been recommended. The snuffling old peke was having trouble with its breathing, the problem had to be tackled and because it was by now a chronic condition a course of **Fluoric Acid** was necessary.

The wily old cross-bred dog, an Old English Sheepdog crossed with a Pyrenean Mountain Dog, now came in looking well groomed and in good shape but the owner appeared to be greatly embarrassed when she came in and was very talkative and took a long time to get down to the fact that this was the family pet and had always been allowed in every room in the home which, being a professional house, had constant visitors. It had now become too embarrassing to have the dog near visitors because of the embarrassing smells that it frequently gave off and despite their wish to have the dog indoors the husband had banned it from the house and it was now faced with an outside existence. Deeply distressed she pleaded for help and so simply came the answer, just **Carbo Veg.** 6 which came to the dog's rescue and the flatus problem was resolved for the dog and consequently for the whole family and happiness was restored.

The next animal for that session was a three months old Golden Retriever puppy which, until the previous day, had been full of lively puppy activity but from teatime had developed signs of runny eyes, slightly runny nose and had all the signs of puppy distemper. How wise that the owner had brought it in so quickly because **Arsenic.Alb.** was immediately produced and it was recommended that **Phosphorus** 30c should be kept handy because it does cover most early cases of distemper. (**Rhus Tox.** 6c can also be administered with great success).
The problems of puppy distemper in the home were immediately alleviated.

Others followed including:
A BULL MASTIFF BITCH. This animal was presented suffering from post season bleeding which had been going on rather longer than normal. Indicated remedies appeared to be either **Millefolium** or **Sabina** but neither of these had any significant effect. It was decided after another two days had elapsed to try **Crotalus Horridus** with the result that the excess bleeding stopped within a few hours. This case illustrates how one remedy will replace another, even though all the ones tried are anti-haemorrhage remedies.
Another SHEEP DOG. This animal had been under the case of various practitioners for the treatment of persistent exzema; this treatment had taken the form of suppressive ointments which had the affect of making the animal lethargic and disinterested to work. The coat had a matted greasy appearance and it was decided to try **Graphites**, which produced a marked improvement.
A COLLIE. This animal was presented with a history of bleeding from the gums, together with occasional vomiting. The temperament was highly nervous and all those symptoms suggested the remedy **Phosphorus** which cured the dog within a few days.
A lovely SETTER BITCH. This was a case of Pyometra which had

taken the form of a chocolate-coloured discharge. Remedies such as **Hydrastis** and **Pulsatilla** had been only partially successful in controlling it, but the remedy **Caulophyllum** produced a lasting response.

Another GREYHOUND BITCH. This animal had developed mastitis after giving birth to dead pups. A foul smelling discharge was present along with sub-normal temperature. Indicated remedy was **Pyrogen** which quickly restored a normal temperature and reduced the discharge. The animal made an uncomplicated recovery.

The fussy CAIRN. This animal was presented with a corneal ulcer in one eye. Remedies such as **Ledum** and **Symphytum** had stabilised the condition but the ulcer did not clear until the remedy **Kali.Bich.** was given.

A nervous POODLE. A history of gravel and red sediment in the urine indicating the need for the remedies **Berberis Vul.** and **Lycopodium** which brought about immediate and lasting improvement.

Next a BOXER. This dog had cystitis which is a common complaint and invariably responds to the remedies **Cantharis** or **Terebinth**, the latter especially when blood appears in the urine.

WEST HIGHLAND TERRIER. This dog had a history of inability to digest food properly, with the result that there was loss of condition. Various examinations had been carried out including an operation and the case had been pronounced incurable owing to replacement of part **of the intenstine with scar tissue. On this basis the remedy Silicea** was employed and the animal then made a steady recovery over a few weeks.

COLLIE. This was a case of post-distemper paralysis which was treated with the remedy **Conium** in various ascending potencies. Recovery took place over a period of six weeks.

ALSATIAN. Presented suffering from acute pneumonia. Remedies such as **Phosphorus** and **Bryonia** produced only partial response but when the remedy **Lycopodium** was given rapid improvement set in and was maintained under different potencies.

COLLIE. This sheep dog was suffering from acute gastro enteritis with haemorrhage stools. These symptoms called for the remedy **Arsenic.Alb.** which quickly relieved.

CORGI. This animal suffered from ear canker in the form of pus discharge together with balanitis and dirty skin. The remedy **Merc. Sol.** quickly produced a lessening of ear symptoms which was maintained under different potencies.

BOXER. Presented suffering from acute urticaria which took the form of large dermatitis plagues on the body. This animal was treated with **Urtica Urens** and quickly responded well.

DACHSHUND. This dog was suffering from alopecia and thickening of the skin inside the front legs. The remedies **Kali. Arsenicum** followed by **Lycopodium** quickly relieved and a lessening of symptoms set in over a few weeks.

RETRIEVER. This was another case of eczema, the animal showing a dry coat with a heavy must smell and severe scratching. It was decided to try the remedy **Psorinum** which produced very satisfying results and the animal quickly grew a thick, healthy coat.

And so, to sum up this canine session our young friend learnt that the various commonly encountered conditions are:-

1) Car sickness when **Cocculus** is the main remedy.
2) Inter digital cysts calling for **Hepar Sul.**, **Graphites**, or **Silicea.**
3) Rheumatic symptoms when remedies such as **Rhus Tox.**, **Ruta Grav.**, or **Bryonia** may be needed.
4) Hysteria or fits which may need **Belladonna.**
5) False pregnancy. Remedies usually employed are **Pulsatilla** and **Sepia.**
6) Wounds and bites. These ask for **Calendula** lotion and the remedy **Ledum** and **Hypericum.**
7) Animals liable to stress or fear usually respond to **Aconitum.**

EAVESDROPPING IN A SURGERY WITH FELINE PROBLEMS

Cats. Let us now visit the surgery for a session on feline problems. Cats are great individualists. No two cats are alike, and because of the variation in their characteristics it is desirable to know much about the particular cat on the surgery table. Because they so cleverly disguise their true personalities in the clinical surroundings of a surgery, it is always to be hoped that an intelligent owner can give something of that particular cat's character as well as its symptoms. So let us sit in at a session with cats.

The first is a yowling, talkative Siamese, expressing its annoyance at the indignity of a journey in a basket. It is suffering from infected ears. An inveterate hunter, it has an infestation of mites gathered from some rabbits' runs. These mites have caused so much irritation that the cat has scratched so violently that the ear flap has blown up into a large blood blister. The recommended treatment for this painful condition is **Arnica** followed by **Bellis Per.**

The second patient is a long-coated Persian stated to be returning most of its food. It is observed that the owner is too casual to be a fit owner for this type of animal, which needs a light grooming daily in order to remove any loose hair. Otherwise the cat, a fastidiously clean animal, licks with its coarse tongue and thus swallows endless hairs which coagulate into hair balls in the throat. Food then cannot easily pass so it is repeatedly sick and finally regurgitates a long roll of hair. The diet of this type of cat is important, a little sunflower seed oil occasionally in its food is helpful and in allaying sickness the suggestions in homoeopathic treatment are **Nux Vom.** or **Carbo Veg.**, both selected according to the needs of the particular cat. Cats do tend to overeat and usually their so called "sickness" is really excess intake therefore a cat's quantity of food should be controlled very carefully.

The lovely old neutered black tom next to arrive is affectionate and friendly and seems quite unaware that the veterinary surgeon is being shown the cat's bare tummy. The anxious owner assures the vet that she does everything to stop him licking and urgently needs help to restore the fur underneath his stomach. This, of course, is the hormone deficiency of the neutered tom and after a very short course of **Natrum Mur.** followed by **Lycopodium** will be happily recovered again. Skin eczema often too arises from a hormone deficiency and, as in dogs, all eczema is slow to clear up, but **Petroleum** or **Merc. Cor.** or **Graphites** are our most popular remedies.

The patient who followed was a rather pathetic tortoiseshell female, speyed and cared for but with a very poor coat and generally lustreless appearance. Worms? Yes! The owner had observed often what looked like rice grains near its tail, the remedy recommended was **Cina** and undoubtedly improvement would soon be noticeable. If on the other hand the cat had tapeworm then the remedy is **Filix Mas.** or **Granatum.**

An emergency! An anxious owner arrives much agitated as her cat has been seen to be knocked by a car as it dashed across the road. It had been rolled into the gutter by the impact and appeared to be dying. The peaceful atmosphere of the surgery calmed both owner and cat. Examination proved that no bones were broken and **Arnica** was quickly administered to alleviate the shock (the same remedy was really needed for the owner!) and this dose repeated at frequent intervals for twelve hours restored the cat to happiness again. Had bones been broken and surgery required then the follow up from Arnica for shock would have been **Symphytum** to help the quicker knitting of the bone.

The very irritable large black and white tom that followed was pawing his face incessantly and endeavouring to rub it on the side of the basket in which it was brought. The Professional immediately observes that there was discomfort in the mouth and that it was probably tartar. On examining the cat (and it is interesting at this point to note how dexterously that mouth was opened) putting the cat firmly on the table; putting his elbow towards the tail and his forearm down the spine; firmly but gently clutching the skin behind the ears between thumb and finger, pulled open the mouth and looking between the mouth and the cheeks it was obvious that the teeth were caked with an encrustation of tartar. This had increased to such an extent that it was pushing onto the gums causing inflammation and, of course, the gums were so sore that everything it attempted to bite caused great pain. It was but a few moments work to get the tartar off the teeth and to reveal nice white dentals underneath, **Strawberry Fragaria** now and in the future will help that cat not to make so much tartar and relieve it of the discomfort that any foreign body on the gums causes.

Cats are usually very clean in their habits and normally a well fed and well trained cat always uses the garden and uses it frequently in some obscure part. It is almost impossible to see from its motion whether in fact it has constipation or whether its bowels are loose or whether it is discharging worms. The owner has to be very observant to note these things, but, of course, there are frequently other signs that the observant owner can notice for constipation, and **Nux. Vomica** or **Carbo. Veg.** would be suggested. For diarrhoea, **Podophyllum** is the tried and trusted and reliable remedy and we have already discussed from a former patient the remedy for worms. A cat's condition is so frequently learned by observing its motions, noticing its appetite and being very careful not to feed it with rabbit bones or chicken bones or anything that will splinter in the course of digestion.

The coughing cat sometimes provides its owner with much anxiety because once a cough starts it tends to continue for a very long time but a very successful remedy is **Rumex** and of course, **Bryonia** so frequently used in chest conditions for humans, and there are other remedies which can be called upon if the cough continues to be very stubborn, as sometimes following distemper or cat 'flu. In cat 'flu the tried remedy is **Arsenicum Alb.**6c, followed up by 30c; **Phosphorus** 30c and finally **Rhus Tox.** cures one of the most frightening illnesses that cats are prone to. These remedies happily avoid side-effects, and quickly restore the cat to health and happiness.

EAVESDROPPING IN A SURGERY TO WHICH CHILDREN BRING THEIR PETS

Let us deal with the children's pets and their problems, by listening in to a period on "Animal care in the schoolroom". Let us hear various questions about peculiar pets that children have, all too often for an unfortunately short time. The budgerigar is the member of the family for which one feels sympathy. Endowed with wings and capable of exhilarating flights in large companies in their natural conditions and haunts, millions are doomed to tiny cages for a life of imprisonment, too often in the smoke laden air of the living room or the cookery smells of the kitchen. The children to whose classroom we have come have many questions about their various budgerigars. The first being a universal question, "Why does my bird peck its feathers. It has none at all down its front and is going bald on the top of its head because it keeps rubbing it on the wires of its cage?"

Mites! The first explanation is probably correct, possibly the bird is irritated by mites and so pecking and rubbing gives it satisfaction. If it is mites, then a spray of powder **Hypericum** diluted 1-10, daily for a week should settle that problem followed by **Sulphur**. But, is the cage infected? This is an important question, for cleanliness is essential for the comfort of any creature and much so for a poor little winged prisoner. The next child has a worry because one of her birds has "a lump under its tummy". This, of course, can be a growth which might even need surgery, in which case **Arnica** in its water before and after such an operation is essential, but we always regard surgery as the last ditch and often **Calcarea Fluorica** in its water will prove efficacious. The second of her two birds has a weepy eye, one eye is often closed. Drips of **Euphrasia** diluted 1 to 10 will usually settle eye troubles in birds or animals and is a good old standby for all problems of this sort.

The third child says her bird often stands with one leg tucked up and sometimes falls off its perch. Has she looked at its claws? Possibly she has not put rough sanded paper or board in the cage to help wear down its claws. Maybe it has cramp due to one thickness of perch. Every cage should have one thick and one thin perch to rest the muscles. Doomed for life to two short lengths of perch, surely it is not asking too much for these to vary in thickness? If cramp is diagnosed the remedy is **Cuprum Met.** in its water. Cuttle fish too is an essential item in the cage, for when the bird is not eating it is often because its beak has become overgrown. Pecking at cuttle fish helps this considerably and provides calcium. The upper beak frequently over-grows the lower one and so it is unable to pick up its food. Starvation is a frequent reason for death in these caged prisoners due to lack of attention to beaks and claws.

Remedies for birds are usually given in the water, if not handleable, but if they will take an opened grape or any sort of soft fruit, then the remedies can be shaken on the fruit in powder form and thus they are gradually taken into the system.

Several children wanted to know about handling their bird. This depends largely on how devotedly they care for it daily and whether the bird is allowed out. If it is, then it should be allowed to perch on a finger. But if, for any reason, the bird has to be held to remove a foreign body from the eye, or wings, then it must be grasped firmly, but not too tightly, in the left hand to leave the right hand free to perform any operation that is necessary. Talking of caged birds, of course, encouraged the children to wander off into their experiences of the little wild birds that they frequently pick up after the cat has mauled them or a car has knocked them, or, in some cases where they fly into a closed window and become stunned. Frequently this happens and the bird can then be held gently in the left hand and diluted **Arnica** trickled down its beak and gently sprayed over its body. If it is going to survive it will usually do so as a result of this treatment but very often the fright has so upset its little heart that it is unable to regain consciousness. I would say that ten per cent only of the injured wild birds live successfully after these various accidents. Opening the beak is not difficult if one feels that force feeding is essential. That is, of course, with the left hand taking the side of the beak from behind the head and pressing it open so that food can be dropped down its throat. But the food must be very loose, very small in quantity in order to prevent the bird from choking. One child wished to have help because her grandmother's parrot had lost its feathers some months ago and although the grandmother had tried various lotions sold to her at the pet shop, nothing made the feathers grow. Was there anything that could be recommended by the veterinary surgeon? Usually the condition is due to an impoverished state and **Selenium** was recommended. Six weeks later there was a very happy report that the quills were coming through and the parrot was no longer morose or sulking but was talking in his old way.

Having spent a long session on bird problems it was a welcome change to have a question on those sensible winter sleepers, the tortoises. The question was, "My tortoise is beginning to move after its winter sleep but its eyes do not seem to be able to open properly yet. How can I help it?" For all simple eye problems the answer is **Euphrasia** dilution 1-10. The tepid bathing in diluted **Calendula** is always a help in this awakening period. Bathe in a shallow container so that the lower shell and as much as possible of the upper one is under this solution for about ten minutes, three times a day for two days. Make sure, of course, that the head is clear of the water.

The little girl who owned three goldfish in a cold water tank was concerned because one of them has a cotton wool like growth. The treatment recommended was to prepare another tank of similar temperature, clean water with a dilution of **Calendula** and so isolate the infected fish from the others as usually this condition arises from poor water. Improved hygiene is equally important as any remedies that can be administered. Moving water, care about not over-crowding, and not over-feeding are the points put to the young owner in answer to her question.

Rabbits. Several of the children have rabbits which are kept at school. To judge from their questions and discussion it would appear that due to confinement in school and not-too-frequently cleaned hutches, most of them were not a hundred per cente fit. Rabbit ear trouble appeared to apply to several of these (so called) pets. Ear canker results from mites found in the ear flaps, this causes extreme irritation with movement. The result is a deposit of crusty debris which if not carefully removed will gradually fill up the canal. Careful cleaning and the application of **Hypericum** 1-10, doses of **Hepar Sulph,** and **Arsenicum Alb.** were recommended. Fleas and mites, to some degree, are tolerated by all rabbits but serious infestations need treatment by **Hepar Sulph.** or **Mer. Corr.** Worms are usually present in all rabbits but signs of loss of condition in the rabbit can usually be traced to an excessive presence of worms and the suggested remedies are **Cina, Filix Mas.** and **Chenopodium.**

Wrong handling of rabbits, that is by the ears instead of handling them by the back of the neck, and supporting the weight of the body by the hand, can often cause spinal troubles or paralysis may result, for which the advised remedies are **Hypericum, Ruta** and **Conium.** Pet rabbits should be groomed but if neglected and hair balls form, then sunflower seed oil is recommended on their food. A fibrous diet is also essential.

Guinea Pigs appeared to be a favourite pet with various children but it was obvious from their conversation that guinea pigs in their care had been very short lived. They are more delicate than rabbits and the conditions in which they are kept are terribly important. They must be kept scrupulously clean and particularly free from draughts. Their diet too has to be watched much more carefully even than that of rabbits and sudden changes of food will affect them very quickly. They can die within a few days, especially if they have been given food that has been out in the winter frost or is something from the deep freeze.

Teeth are a problem in guinea pigs, especially where their diet lacks roughage. Regretfully the teeth have to be clipped as necessary. The diet must be watched and overcrowding or boredom will also cause a good deal of fur-chewing, not so much on themselves but on other inhabitants of the colony. Overcrowding is a cause of much trouble and the keeping of guinea pigs has to be guided very carefully. Pneumonia, for which the remedy is **Phosphorus** or **Bryonia** or **Ant. Tart.** depending on type, can affect all the animals and they show signs of having a cold and lie about unwilling to eat. This complaint can be due to poor housing or lack of ventilation and can all too often prove fatal but, hopefully, can be helped by isolating any of the animals that appear to be unfit. Skin conditions too are due to wrong diet and are not easy to cure. Wherever there is an infestation of lice or fleas a bath or dip is frequently necessary as guinea pig skin does not react to the usual treatment such as given to cats or rabbits. Fortunately they very rarely suffer from ear trouble.

Hamsters, those fascinating little creatures, were only owned by one child and that particular child's pet had had the usual teething trouble caused through lack of suitable caging. It is essential that they have something hard to gnaw on. Likely the little creature is fed too much on the same foods as the humans. This is, of course, completely unsuitable, apart from the fact that in the case of these little creatures the cheek pouches are very large and some food will inevitably get caught inside and cause a lot of discomfort. It should be emptied out and flushed out with plain water but great care is needed in the handling of hamsters. Kidney trouble is not uncommon in hamsters and the treatment recommended for this is **Nat. Mur.** or **Apis Mel.**

Gerbils. In this case the school itself had its little colony of gerbils in which the children took quite a lot of interest and were properly trained to handle them correctly. But all seemed to have dry coats and rather scaly condition which, of course, demanded first a variation in the diet. It was suggested that **Arsenic. Alb.** should be introduced into their water or powdered **Sulphur** or **Selenium** put on to their food. One had a small tumor but it was not regarded as something that was of a serious nature and the children were quite happy to change the diet for this particular little colony which was properly housed and treat them with more regular interest.

The problem with children's pets is that children lose interest and need guidance and inspiration from adults in order that they will remain loyal to their pets over a long period.

EAVESDROPPING OUT OF DOORS

Now let us go to the Farm School arranged as a Rural Community Training for the older boys. Here, of course, we find the large animals, the ponies, donkeys, goats etc., and the boys greet the veterinary surgeon with countless problems that they have met with the various animals. The ponies are causing problems because, as it has been a very dry hard summer, this has caused hoof trouble and soreness which has developed into laminitis. The remedies for this, although simple, demand a good deal of patience and the veterinary surgeon prescribed **Aconitum, Belladonna** and **Calcarea Fluor.** There are two or three of the ponies with continued skin trouble, the result of the spring itch that is reluctant to clear up, and, of course, many ponies suffer from eye trouble during these hot dry spells. **Arsenic.Alb.** and **Silicea** usually help.

The girls came along with their ponies, several of which are suffering from saddle sores due largely to the modern plastic saddle. This does not mould to the body as the good old hand made leather ones used to and **Hepar Sulph.** and **Calendula** 1-10 will help.

The donkey acts as companion to these ponies when some go away for riding lessons or are sold. He is always there as the friend of those who remain. He has eye trouble and the treatment is recommended. But his skin trouble is of rather a different nature because he has been over-fed with oats and has been stealing the food given to the horses. The donkey's diet is very important. He needs a rough type of food that is found in say, blackberry brambles and that type of land, rather than meadow hay. The remedies for this are **Nux. Vom.** and **Rhus Tox.**
One of the goats has mastitis and two of them have diarrhoea. This is largely attributable to the recent weather but, nevertheless, has to be treated over a fairly long period — **Arsenic. Alb** and **Cina** will help.

From early childhood, as one who has been brought up in homoe-opathy, I learnt that wherever you go and whatever your needs there are six homoeopathic remedies which should always be at hand. Between them they are capable of covering most of the illnesses or problems that can arise on holidays or in the home and all are useful when there are no other remedies to hand. The childhood remedies remain; we must always have three "A's", two "B's" and one "C". These are: **Arnica, Arsenicum, Apis, Belladonna, Bryonia** and **Calendula**. Perhaps it would be helpful to explain a little more about each of these and their uses so that the animal owner at least can have these six handy and do a great deal in helping the animal not to suffer. Peter collected seven most useful remedies in the 30 potency thus beginning to accumulate his own homoeopathic First Aid kit. They included:-

ACONITE

In Aconite preparations the whole of the plant is used, it is known to the botanist as Monkshood. This remedy is very efficacious for use with the nervous or excited dog which cannot sleep and barks continuously. Indeed, any indication from any animal or person of terror and restlessness can be guaranteed to be relieved by **Aconite**. Physical and mental restlessness both call for its use, especially in the beginning of acute diseases. However it does not carry on over a long period and should not be continued after there is a pathological change. The dog about to suffer from distemper, which shows dullness and loss of appetite and dull eyes and rapid pulse, should be taken quickly in hand with doses of **Aconite** every 2 or 3 hours. This also applies to the highly strung and nervous horse who is startled at the slightest movement and has a rapid pulse. Always resorting to **Aconite** at the start of any illness proves to be a safe and helpful remedy.

A nervous Siamese cat recently transported to a new home or into Boarding Kennels, that has become restless and constantly crying can be readily soothed by three doses of **Aconite** 6 or 30 during the first day.

ARSENICUM

This wide-ranging remedy demands a place in every homoe-opathic kit for animals. Its application is particularly useful in skin troubles including mange and eczema. Its success with internal disorders; distemper, enteritis and gastritis have long since been proved. One small Scottish Terrier which had worried its owner for months because its coat was poor and its skin dry and scaly, became completely presentable after three days treatment followed by three days rest over a period of one month using **Arsenicum** 6c.

ARNICA

This plant is indigenous to mountain plateaus and it flourishes in Switzerland. The flowers and the root of the plant have the most pronounced medicinal properties.

No family medicine chest can afford to be without **Arnica**. It is the ever ready remedy for bruises and tumbles experienced by the children of the home and the strains and sprains of the adult who falls from the ladder, the bicycle or the horse. An immediate application of diluted tincture (five drops per wine glass of water) gently sipped will lower the shock and if applied to the bruised parts will reduce the pain and prevent discolouration. In injuries to the eye in the animal or the human, there will be no black eye if it is quickly applied after the injury, for **Arnica** stops the effusion of blood. There may be some slight discolouration but not the deep purple swelling.

The over-worked muscles after a day of unusually heavy work such as gardening can be given considerable ease by a tablespoonful of **Arnica** in a hot bath. The animals response to **Arnica** is exceptionally noticeable if one tablet of 30 potency is given every hour before an operation and followed by three further tablets every four hours after the operation. It is similarly very efficacious for both humans and animals both preceeding and following dental extractions. The injured animal in an accident will suffer much less acutely if **Arnica** is trickled into its mouth while awaiting the veterinary surgeon and all frights and fears can be arrested by its administration. If the animal has been seriously bruised by being knocked over by a car but has no broken flesh or bones then the gentle bath of **Arnica** has quite remarkable results.

Often too, the bird rescued from the family cat responds promptly to spots of **Arnica** gently trickled into the beak from the ever handy pipette. The starling that flew into the motorists windscreen and gave every appearance of death was in fact concussed and the promptly given **Arnica** (always carried in the car in the event of such emergencies) enabled wings to spread for a happy take-off. An unforgettable experience was with a dog when it had been romping about at great speed in the snow. It then came indoors and was allowed too near the fire so that the pads became sore and uncomfortable. The dog attacked the pads by frantic biting because, presumably, they were irritating and having much the same effect to the dog as chilblains would have to the human. Cotton wool soaked in **Arnica** put on the pads regularly over a period of several hours completely cured the unhappy condition. **Arnica** is ever present for any bruises or trouble that is not affected by broken skin, when of course, one goes to **Calendula.**

APIS

Apis is the bee sting and is in fact a compound of bee sting or even the whole of the dried bee's body. One's memory goes to **Apis** whenever there is a sting and the dog that has snapped at a wasp and been stung can be given almost immediate relief if a dose of **Apis** 6 or 30 is administered quickly. This applies too if the dog disturbs an ants nest and has been attacked by them. It also has great uses in any cases of inflammation, so that mastitis and acute nephritis are both very readily eased by the use of **Apis** which is a good stand-by in the homoeopathic homely medicine chest.

BELLADONNA

Commonly known to us as Deadly Nightshade, this is a very active and much used remedy and has a quickly marked action in skin and glands. We also associate its valuable use in epileptic spasms. The excitable poodle that frequently had a certain amount of nausea, vomiting and was hysterically barking and even becoming violent in its excitement, was brought into the veterinary surgery to be put to sleep. The owner could no longer stand its irresponsible behaviour. **Belladonna** was administered, three doses daily of 6c gradually reduced to two doses and then finally one per day as the trouble abated. The dog remained a perfectly calm and happy little dog for the rest of its life.

BRYONIA

There are many varieties but we are most familiar with the White Bryony which grows in most of our hedgerows and can be used as an external application for bruises but is more frequently used in animals who have a cough and for all kinds of rheumatism, stiffness in the joints and can deal very successfully with bronchitis and dyspepsia. It is a very all-round helper in many ailments from which the larger dog tends to suffer. A Great Dane that had had every kind of treatment and possessed almost every illness from which dogs could suffer was made into a perfectly normal animal with no rheumatism, no cough, no digestive troubles, simply on a course of **Bryonia** 30 over a period of six weeks.

CALENDULA (Marigold)

Whether in the home, where there are one or two animals, or in the large Kennels where there are a large number, it is quite certain that **Calendula** has to be called into use almost daily. The minor cuts, the results of fights, the torn eyelid, the tendencies to haemorrhage can all be tackled by internal and external solutions of **Calendula**. The healing properties of the Marigold are well known to those who work constantly with animals and often **Calendula** can be used when **Arnica** has to be avoided. **Calendula** can be used where the skin is broken and this definitely does not apply to **Arnica.** It relieves the severest pains attending various accidents and it is invaluable in ulcers of the legs and pads of the dog such as can occur in the older animal. With affections of the eyelids, 20 drops to a teacup full of water can form a lotion to be used for two or three days by its frequent application in cotton wool. Where haemorrhage is considerable, the lotion, of course, should be much stronger. There is no broken skin problem that **Calendula** does not hastily help.

From his long term of standing in at surgeries and asking countless questions of Uncle George our young friend, Peter, was beginning to gather a very sound basic knowledge of homoeopathic treatment and gradually thought only in terms of homoeopathy when he or his animals or his friends in the school playground were in need of some sort of medication. What, therefore, was his delight when during one vacation (when he had finally decided that on leaving school he must become a veterinary surgeon and study Homoeopathy), he learnt that the local radio was putting on a whole series of questions in connection with homoeopathy which they called a "Phone-In". There was a series of six half-hours when the general public were invited to phone in and Uncle George was to be available to answer their questions. Peter had his pen poised throughout and learned so many of the remedies that had been advised. He asked further questions about them to such an extent that his knowledge and memory of homoeopathy became increasingly extended. These questions are now to follow but they have been sorted out into categories of dogs, cats etc. Of course, the questions as they came in covered a multiplicity of types of animals but it is easier to have help from these questions by reading them out of the sequence that they were given. We will proceed with the questions on cats. Of necessity, therefore, there will be repetition of things already read in this book but since homoeopathy needs oft repeating and oft learning it will, perhaps, be helpful to have this repetition. Through all homoeopathic treatment is must always be remembered that it is the personality that is being treated rather than the actual body that is being examined. Consequently, the hairy old sheepdog suffering from exactly the same complaint as the very trim Jack Russell, may need the same type of remedy but not the actual named remedy that is discussed here. It is the comparable one that must be looked for and most books on homoeopathy will give the alternative where it is wise to do so. Always "Like with Like" must be the guiding principle and this demands a deep study of symptoms as well as the student's concentration on the variety of remedies available.

The flood of correspondence that followed these "Phone-Ins" was overwhelming to the over-stressed Uncle George. But it was of great excitement to Peter who, with no responsibility to write the hundreds of answers, found the queries very interesting. He became highly incensed by a few rude and some critical comments from those who were sceptical or plainly biased, or definitely in opposition to homoeopathic treatment.

He selected the letters that were genuinely seeking further help. many of interest from people who were already converts to homoeopathic medicine and wished to add stories of their own successes in order to encourage others.

The many questions that were asked proved of much interest to Peter who carefully noted all the answers that were given and Peter felt that it was of interest to copy down all the questions and to give the answers as dictated by Uncle George.

QUESTIONS ABOUT CATS

My neutered tom is 7 years old and is very fit but he constantly licks his tummy and is now without hair over a large patch there, although the skin looks clear and healthy. What would be the best treatment.

NATRUM MUR. 30. 3 a day for 4 days followed by **LYCOPODIUM** 6 2 a day for 7 days.

My cat has a sort of lower eyelid which has appeared to both his eyes. He appears to be fairly well but is pernickety over his food whereas formerly he had a good appetite.

NAT. MUR. 10m repeat only as necessary.

My cat seems to be worried about his cheeks which he frequently paws. He has not, so far, scratched his cheeks seriously but there is some discomfort and no apparent skin trouble. What could this be?

The symptoms are being caused by Tartar and the remedy is: **STRAWBERRY FRAGARIA** 6 for 4 days — Repeat periodically if needed.

My cat's motion is clay coloured, he is fairly often sick after a meal and yet enjoys his food. How can I treat him to prevent this?

PHOSPHORUS 30c. daily for as long as is necessary. Watch for improvement and then cease the remedy.

My old cat dribbles almost constantly but does not sneeze or appear to be in pain. This is rather unpleasant in the house and although we would like to keep him we cannot do so if the dribbling persists.

MERC. SOL. 30c 2 per day for 7 days and watch for progress.

How would I know if my cat was developing cat 'flu. I am nervous of any such illness which I understand can be fatal but I fear I should not notice the early symptoms.

There would be runny eyes, sneezing and coughing. **ACONITUM** 30c.

Although my cat seems fairly contented and eats well, he is drinking an abnormal amount, sometimes a pint in the course of a day. Why is this and is there anything I can do to reduce the liquid intake?

The cat may be diabetic or there could be a kidney weakness. If the latter try: **NAT. MUR.** 10m repeat 3 times weekly until improvement sets in.

Diabetes has been diagnosed in our cat and although we are using insulin the condition is proving very difficult to stabilise. Is there a homoeopathic remedy to help?

SYZYGIUM 1x. daily — watch progress and continue as necessary.

I have got to take my very nervous cat to the veterinary surgery to be speyed. Is there anything I can give her to combat her nervousness?

ACONITUM 12c the morning and evening before the journey.

My old cat is 15 years old and her liver is giving out. Apart from this she seems quite healthy and not in pain but she has lost a lot of weight although she eats well. Is there something to ease her condition?

LYCOPODIUM 30c will nearly always ease this condition.

My 12 year old Siamese had a slight stroke last year and has a weak heart, what can I do to help her?

Strokes are very frequently remedied or arrested by: **CRATAEGUS** 3c or **CONIUM** 30c. daily for a given period.

Last night my cat got run over and although the vet says there is nothing broken, she is still terrified, shaking and will not eat or drink.

A period of treating with **ACONITUM** followed by **ARNICA** 30c.

I gave a home to an unwanted kitten 3 weeks ago but he is still very weak and exceptionally small. Is there anything I can give him to make him stronger?

LYCOPODIUM 12c is the recommended remedy until improved.

My elderly cat is constantly thirsty and passing more urine than usual, this presumably is her kidneys failing. What help can be given?

NAT. MUR. 200c for a period followed by 10m.

My kitten has dry scaly patches, circular in shape mostly on the ears and paws. Is this ringworm and what treatment can be given?

This would appear to be Ringworm and the remedy would be: **BACILLINUM** 200c.

My cat has developed sore, itching, weeping patches along its spine. How best can this be treated and what is the probable cause?

This is probably hormonal in origin and the remedy here is: **FOLLICULINUM** 30c

Following a fight my cat has a large swelling on his face which looks like an abscess which has discharged but has an unpleasant smell. What would be the best treatment.

SILICEA 200c. 3 times weekly for 4 weeks is best used here.

QUESTIONS ABOUT DOGS

My 7 month old Alsatian bitch is having diarrhoea problems. I have taken her off red meat which only helped for a time. I have now put her on to meal but this is not helping either. She is a restless dog, what would be the best treatment?

The remedy here would be **ARSENIC. ALB.** 30c until symptoms subside.

My speyed bitch has a soft growth on her back about the size of a golf ball. Should this be removed surgically?

Try the remedy: **CALC. FLUOR.** 30c.

This morning my dog passed a motion containing worms, I am not sure whether it is a tape worm or round worm. What treatment can I give?

For Tapeworm the remedy is: **FILIX MAS** 3x
For Roundworm: **CHENOPODIUM** 3c.

My dog hates car travel and yet adores getting into the car but once the engine starts she howls and is very frightened. What travel sickness remedy is best for a dog of this type?

There are two main remedies here: **COCCULUS** 6c and **ARGENT.NIT.** 12c.

My 3 year old mongrel bitch constantly has false pregnancies when she takes to mothering her toys etc. Is speying the answer or how can she best be treated?

PULSATILLA 12c should be given followed by **SEPIA** 30c.

My rescued Alsatian hates men with beards. My husband has a beard and this has become a serious problem, must he shave his beard off or have you any other suggestion?

Try the remedy: **ARGENT. NIT.** 12c.

My 2 year old Jack Russell is hyperactive despite having the freedom of the garden and long walks. What treatment would be helpful to calm him down?

TARENTULA HISP. 12c should be given.

My elderly Yorkshire Terrier has become incontinent during the night time although he is clean during the day. Can anything help him?

The hormone remedy: **A.C.T.H.** 30c should be administered.

My dog has bad breath but there is no evidence of tooth decay or infection of the gums. Can it be some form of indigestion and if so what treatment do you recommend?

The tried and trusted remedy here would be: **CARBO VEG.** 200c.

My Whippet was rescued and obviously has been mistreated in the past. In his own environment he is perfectly happy but in a foreign situation he shakes continuously and is obviously distressed. What would be the best treatment?

GELSEMIUM 200c should be given until symptoms subside.

My Spaniel has persistent ear irritation despite having ear drops regularly. What can be done to help this situation?

TELLURIUM 12c is the remedy to be used here.

My St. Bernard has arthritis in his back legs which occurs particularly in cold weather. What is the best remedy to use?

RHUS TOX. 6c should be given followed by **RHUS TOX.** 1m.

My beloved Cairn terrier has had cancer diagnosed. Naturally I do not want to have her put to sleep, is there any advice that will be helpful?

CADMIUM SULPH. 12c should be tried here.

We have lately boarded our dog in a very nice Kennel but unfortunately he has come home with Kennel Cough. Is there anything that we can do to cure this and any advice we can give to the Kennels in order to prevent it happening to their dogs and others?

The remedy here is **COCCUS CACTI** 6c. There is a homoeopathic oral vaccine available which the Kennels could use.

Our Chow has chronic eczema which seemed to start when he picked up fleas. We have cleared the fleas but the eczema remains, what help can you give?

SULPHUR 30c is the useful skin remedy and **SELENIUM** 30c may also be used.

Our dog is very contented and happy in between his attacks of epilepsy, however we can find no way of controlling his fits. Is there a remedy which can help?

There are many remedies which could be used and: **BELLADONNA** or **CUPRUM** are two very useful ones.

QUESTIONS ABOUT HORSES

I have a pony that I keep out in a paddock which has a stream running at the bottom and the field gets very damp and my pony has gone lame and mud fever has been diagnosed. What can I give it to cure this?

MALANDRINUM 30c or **GRAPHITES** 12c can be used here.

Three girls have three horses which are stabled together. They cough a great deal and we are told it is because they are stabled a lot. What can we do to cure this coughing?

BRYONIA 30c is the remedy widely used for coughs or **BERYLLIUM** 30c.

The farrier says my horse is a "crib-biter" I pay to have him stabled and I am in trouble because he has done a lot of damage to the door and the wooden rails inside. Is there anything I can do to stop this habit?

This is not easy as it is a vice but **LYCOPODIUM** 1m can be tried.

My horse is very difficult to transport. It gets very nervous and is also nervous in traffic and has a particular fear of road signs. Is there a remedy to help this?

ACONITUM 30c and **ARGENT.NIT.** 12c are remedies which will help here.

My horse ran into some spikes near a gate-post and has abrasions. What is the best treatment for this.

HYPERICUM lotion 1/10 should be administered to the wounds and **ARNICA** 12c taken internally.

My horse has rubbing and bruising under the saddle and also sore places which a friend says is "girth gall". Is there anything I can give it for this?

The remedy indicated here is **HEPAR SULPH.** 30c.

I find my pony has "rain rash", what treatment would you advise?

This calls for **ARSENIC. ALB.** 200c.

If my horse develops colic, apart from keeping it from rolling, is there any medication that would help?

The main remedy for colic is **COLOCYNTHIS** 1m.

Whilst cleaning my horse's feet out I find it has thrush. What would be the best treatment?

KREOSOTUM 200c is the remedy called for here.

Every summer my pony gets "sweet itch" and is worried by flies. How can this be treated?

A very useful remedy for this is **ARSENIC.ALB.** 30c, 200c or 1m.

What can I give my horse to help strained tendons?

RHUS TOX. 1m will get good response but if not then **RHUS VEN.** 1m should be given.

My horse has some warts on its face and as the face is a very sensitive area, what can you recommend?

The remedy here is **THUJA** 30c taken internally and also **THUJA** lotion applied to the warts.

GENERAL QUESTIONS

My tropical fish have developed a film over their eyes and a few of them have died after a few days. Is there anything I can put in their water to save the remainder of them?

Try the remedy **SILICEA** 30c or **CALC.FLUOR** 30c.

One of my ducks has an infection above its beak. What would be the best treatment as it appears to be an abscess which has not discharged?

An abcess will usually respond very well to **HEPAR SULPH.** 6c.

My two guinea pigs have recently started scratching and have bald patches appearing on their backs. Can you advise some treatment please?

Various forms of skin problems respond well to **SELENIUM** 30c.

My rabbits have been fighting and one of them has a nasty abscess on his back. What should I put in the water to heal it up?

A useful remedy here is **SILICEA** 30c.

My tortoise has just awakened from hibernation but has not yet started eating. Ought I to do something to give him an appetite?

A good remedy for a sluggish digestive system is **NUX VOM.** 6c.

My parrot has become very nervous and refuses to come out of its cage and has also started to pull all its feathers out. Your advice would be greatly valued?

The remedy indicated here is **ARGENT.NIT.** 12c.

My budgerigar keeps falling off his perch and walking in circles round the bottom of the cage. He is only 2 years old, is there anything he can be given to cure this?

This condition will be greatly helped by **AGARICUS** 30c.

My guinea pig has pined and now refuses to eat since the death of the rabbit who was his constant companion. What can I do to encourage his appetite and cheer him up.

IGNATIA 12c is the remedy which is used in times of loss such as this.

My tame Jackdaw has just been mauled by a cat and is in a state of shock. He has a wound on his chest but no broken bones. What is the best treatment?

ACONITUM 30c should be given followed by **ARNICA** 30c.

POTENCIES

Following these "Phone-Ins" several requests came from clubs or similar groups of people asking if they could have speakers. They were anxious to learn more of the advantages of the alternatives to the drugs commonly administered and which they had proved so often left unpleasing side-effects. All this was more work for Uncle George but, most exciting of all, Peter's School Parent Teachers Association wanted a debate on the subject! This was decided upon and enabled Peter to prepare his case for Homoeopathy and to endeavour to explain what had now become to him the healing magic of homoeopathy for animals. Among other pupils in the school were the sons of two very orthodox doctors and a biased chemist's son, so the stage was well set for a heated and valuable discussion. This, of course, inspired the enthusiasm of Peter to get the co-operation of Uncle George but withal to phrase his paper entirely in his own language and style, to give the subject in his own way to those in his own age range. Readily he had to hand many examples of where orthodox drugs had failed and homoeopathy had succeeded; many stories were quickly available to his memory. He recalled the irascible white Pekinese who raised its leg to "spend a penny" but could not get it down again as his back had "gone". He was so beautiful everyone wanted to cuddle him and everyone got bitten for their efforts, including his mistress but he fell in love with the homoeopathic doctor who suggested the 10m of **Ruta,** which cured him. There was also the Apso puppy who could not go out because her feet had been stung by the newly emerging spring nettles. Her owners were wonderously impressed when after giving half a dozen granules of **Urtica** 30 she never had any more trouble. Then there was Beth, the collie who was never able to travel without severe car sickness and had been left out of family outings altogether until **Nux Vomica** 30 was given on one or two occasions before a journey. She was never car sick again and never needed any more **Nux Vomica.** Her love of the car became greater than her love of walkies. Once Beth had a nasty scratch of the cornea, which began to cloud over. The owner dreaded blindness and rushed to the homoeopathic doctor who administered **Ledum** 200 followed by **Ruta** 6 and the eye was soon perfect.

At the meeting questions of the small (the minute) dose were hurled at Peter and the art and science of Homoeopathy, being so unlike orthodox medicine, it became necessary to explain what is meant by "potencies". He explained that it is really the breaking down of a drug or the sucussing or vigorously shaking of it all embraced by the word "potentising" which really means the release of the power within the drug. The process of potentising he endeavoured to explain is achieved by diluting a drug by adding to it a quantity of water or alcohol in proportions of one of the drug to ninety nine of the water or alcohol and shaking vigorously (or rubbing down if it is a metal). This shaking or sucussing or grinding breaks down the substance of the drug and releases from it the "atomic" energy. These dilutions follow a definite plan. The first potency is made by taking one measured drop of the drug and diluting it with ninety nine drops of alcohol and shaking it vigorously. Then the second potency is produced by taking one drop of the first potency, adding to that ninety nine drops of alcohol and again sucussing and this process can be repeated always in similar proportions and always providing sufficient shaking to release the power within the substance of the drug. Each vigorous shaking in turn releasing more completely the latent power of the drug. This latent power is therefore the more capable of being of service to the Active Force of the animal's body or of the humans.

At first he himself found the efficacy of the very minute dose so difficult to understand that he was determined to endeavour to simplify it for those who were listening to him because he was well aware that they were listening very critically. The debate was exhilarating, the "anti's" quibbled that it was all in the mind, that people would believe anything, would accept any advertisement if it were repeated often enough and with sufficient confidence but Peter quickly argued that it cannot be faith and imagination in the mind of the animal. The bird does not think when it has fallen with concussion, "**Arnica** will make me better" it just gets better after **Arnica** has been administered. An orthodox critic asked why, if down the years doctors had found what drugs to use for certain illnesses why now should Homoeopathy come up with the mad idea that a hundredth or even a thousandth part of that same drug should be more efficacious? Perhaps Peter's reply seems to be over-simplified but his acceptance of the reality of the Active Force which represents each one of us as our own real individual self, and his interpretation now had come to mean to him the same as the words Life Force. Every plant, every tree, every body whether human, animal, fish or bird, all the world, all the universe and all that therein is combined in his study of Homoeopathy as the one great Active Force permeating and being "everything". Not only does it control every individual but **all** of every individual and in Peter's early solving of the mysteries of the minute doses and the efficacy of the almost non-existent dose of a remedy, became all clear to him as he saw the wonderful spirituality of the great Active Force as being only able to use its force in healing the Diseases of the body it controls, and fighting the attacking illness to that body, with frequently sucussed plant, that being the "like" remedy for the "like disease". Only by repeated sucucsion of the necessary plant could its highly Active Force be sufficiently released to become the remedy for the malady which would be used by the Active Force within the body. To give a simplified example, a mountaineer had become detached from his guide's rope and rolled down the mountain as if to his death. He was rescued from a ledge but was grievously shaken and terribly bruised. Immediately his own Active Force took over but needed the support of a highly sucussed plant **Arnica** which was promptly administered with good results. This accident, being in the Swiss Alps he would probably have been surrounded by **Arnica** plants but mastication of its leaves and roots would not have helped. It was the Active Force released from that plant by the constant pounding or sucussing which was now imperative for his Active Force to be able to take over and fight the attacking bruising and pain with the highly potentised **Arnica.**

These highly diluted drugs can be used more capably by the experienced homoeopath and it is generally recommended that the 6th potency or the 30th potency are the wisest to be used on animals particularly in the hands of lay workers. Peter endeavoured to reiterate the importance of realising the power of the minute dose. Until people come to accept the fact that life is the Universal Force everywhere and in everything they will never be able to accept the equally Universal Power of the highly sucussed drug being in cooperation with the active force of the animal or the human.

Many questions in the discussion referred to the boys' own problems with their pets and Peter had at least the satisfaction of having made now a really good try to interest them. He hoped that his devotion to this alternative to orthodox drugs would now be understood by some of his audience. He laboured too the fact that no laboratory experiments are ever needed to be carried out on animals or humans which are to be treated by homoeopathy. While looking at all the pills and potions and powders in the homoeopathic surgery of Uncle George there was great satisfaction that not one of them had to be tried out on a suffering animal in an experimental laboratory. That alone proved a great recommendation to some of his listeners who were already horrified by information that they had gleaned elsewhere about medical experiments performed on animals in the laboratories up and down the country.

The sceptics in his audience were in the minority. Parents and teachers sensed his enthusiasm and his obvious sincerity and several were already deciding to follow up his talk by further reading. Two were anxious to get professional advice for long-standing health problems in their own animals which so far orthodox treatment had failed to cure. One interesting outcome of the evening was an invitation to any who were interested, to visit an animal welfare centre where the patients were predominantly treated by homoeopathic methods. The date selected for this visit was a bright morning in May and on arrival, far from being left to wander the fields without an organised conductor, they were conducted around the centre and their interest was arrested at the surgery where by chance a little white West Highland dog was just having dental treatment. It had come into the Centre discarded and had an abscess under its eye. The veterinary surgeon traced the abscess to tooth trouble and discovered that a former treatment had broken off a tooth instead of extracting it and this had caused the very painful abscess. So, the little animal had to be anaesthetised but not until **Arnica** had been administered and given long enough for the **Arnica** to help with any sort of fear or shock the animal was likely to be experiencing. The **Arnica** having been given they were interested in hearing stories of other animals that had recently had treatment. When a little time had passed they then watched with much interest the tooth being extracted and the veterinary surgeon discovering that the comparable tooth on the other side was in like condition of disrepair and that too was extracted. Later, after they had wandered the Sanctuary, they returned to see the little dog coming round from its operation with more **Arnica** being administered. This would continue for a day or so until the animal was completely recovered. Undoubtedly the administration of the **Arnica** had greatly helped as it does in humans or animals to reduce the suffering, the fear and the troubles that one asociates with "going to the dentist" or any operation.

The little company was then conducted up to what was known as the October Field. There, grazing happily, were various donkeys in little groups of twos or threes. One, however, was on its own, awaiting treatment for a skin condition. This animal had just lately come in and had been in what the former owners would have claimed to be a nice kind home. Their kindness was very mistaken for it had been fed on all the wrong kinds of foods, quite a lot of buns, rolls, sweet things and very little coarse hay and brambles. What a donkey really needs is roughage rather than soft food such as given to a race horse. This meant that there had to be a fairly long period of treatment before the donkey could grow a good coat. At the moment it was in knotted tufts where it had rubbed itself on tree trunks and gate posts because it was itching and uncomfortable. The remedies supplied were **Arsenic.Alb.** 30c for 21 days following by **Nux Vom.** until improvement had set in.

As they walked the fifteen acres round the lake and saw several hundred ducks, geese, swans, peacocks, hens and bantams, it was interesting that they spotted among this large number the few disabled ones. They were reminded that all had come in unwanted or discarded. Some were found on the roadside or in trouble following accidents and had arrived in difficulty.

Two or three with bumble foot were being treated and even one enjoying life happily despite the fact that it was minus a leg. A bird of any type can exist with one leg but cannot be nearly so happy if it is minus a wing. The duck that they observed was nearly blind was a matter for concern, but as it stayed close to its companion, so the two appeared to enjoy life, to find food and freedom and happiness.

Various other problems arose in the walk around the Sanctuary. Bumble foot in hens which causes swelling in the joint was noticed to be being treated with **Calc.Fluor.** 30c, one three times per week for six weeks. A traumatic eye injury to a duck following a fight was benefitting from **Ledum** 6c, one daily for ten days followed by **Symphytum** 200c, one three times weekly for four weeks.

General veterinary problems occurred as questions and these included:-

SPANIEL EAR — a chronic recurrent moist otitis the cause of which is usually a mixture of bacteria and fungii, so while conventional treatment settles the problem temporarily by attacking one element of the problem, secondary flare-ups result when one of the other elements takes over. The remedy here would be **Merc.Sol.** 6c twice daily for 21 days.

EPILEPSY IN DOGS — control is possible but drugs are constantly required. It should be noted that some conditions which are diagnosed as primary epilepsy are in fact a result of Lead poisoning. **Cuprum Met.** 30c, one daily for thirty days, if Lead poisoning is suspected then **Plumbum** 30c daily for thirty days should be administered,

CHRONIC CAT 'FLU — seen mainly in Siamese and other highly bred cats, where low grade 'flu infection persists and the cat seems unable to "throw off" the infection. The remedy here would be **Kali Bich.** 200c one three times per week for four weeks.

LIP FOLD PYODERMA — a chronic moist dermatitis seen in Spaniels and others who have folds of flesh around the face and mouth. **Hepar Sulph.** 30c at a dose of one per day for 21 days followed by 200c three times per week for four weeks.

The walk round the Sanctuary and fields, the lingering ambles among the variety of animals continued throughout the day. Countless notes were enthusiastically made and the little company left with added enthusiasm and deepened interest in animals and their needs. In their notebooks they had a store of simple remedies for a variety of problems that their own animal's health could present.

Having returned home and talked of their experiences to

neighbours, they met some ignorance and some opposition to the alternative methods about which they were now learning. The opposition usually evaporated as successes could be unmistakeably proved. One instance was the woman who had not visited her veterinary surgeon over a particular problem but had taken the advice and made purchases of what was possibly by name the correct remedy. The pet showed no improvement and finally Uncle George's help was sought and he provided his own carefully sucussed and thoughtfully planned potency of the correct remedy with the same name. The animal improved but the owner, still sceptical about Homoeopathy, moaned that what she had obtained from the Pet Shop and what had been provided by Uncle George both looked and tasted the same, for she had tasted both! Much explanation then had to follow to try to convince her that a homoeopathically sucussed remedy could in no way be compared with something bought over the shop counter after seeing an advertisement of television!

HOW HOMOEOPATHY RESURRECTED "CHICKEN LITTLE." —

Among items of literature given to him at the Raystede Centre for Animal Welfare Peter found a contribution by Ron Parker, one of the staff. He enjoyed reading it to his group of friends at school for it typifies the success of homoeopathy when carefully administered.

One evening as dusk had fallen in early January I noticed a very small bantam hen which had been severely attacked about the head and was in a very bad state. I placed it in a cage in safety but in the morning it was lying stiff and cold apparently dead. Sadly, I brought the little bird down to the surgery, when I suspected that I felt a very slight twitching movement, which was hardly noticeable and did not seem to repeat. I washed its eyes in **Euphrasia** and administered 5 drops of **Arnica** in water through a dropper and bathed the head wound in a solution of five drops of **Calendula** in warm water, then placed the bird in a small box on the radiator. Every half hour I opened its beak and fed it with a solution of honey and glucose in hot water to which had been added a crushed tablet of **Aconite.**

There was no movement for at least 3 hours and it was indeed 6 hours before it attempted to raise its head. With great relief I watched this very slight improvement but it was time for me to go home so I took it with me in a box of straw so that I could continue the treatment through the evening and night. Up until 11 o'clock I could still only feed it through the dropper but, twenty-four hours later, I found it could actually stand! One eye was still closed and I covered the wound on the head with **Calendula** ointment. I was by now feeding it with wholemeal bread soaked in honey and glucose water with a pair of tweezers. The next day on the wound I lightly smoothed **Arnica** ointment and this included the eye-lid because the eye was still closed and was surrounded by bruising.

After 3 days the other eye started to open and it made a small effort to feed itself. I then placed with it a small amount of chick corn in the box but continued to feed it with soaked bread and glucose. After another week it started to feed itself and was by now enjoying peeled grapes and meal worms in its diet. The head wound is a clean healthy pink now but it will be some time before it really grows its feathers. First I called it "Little Chicken" but this had become "Chicken Little", for after another seven days it is now a lusty little creature happily responding to its name and feeding itself with great eagerness. Such is the satisfaction of the opportunity we have at Raystede to care for even the smallest suffering creature.

Now another half term was ending and the time had come for Peter and several of his age range to make the final decision as to what course their future was to take. Peter unhesitatingly settled for veterinary work which destined him to a long and expensive training. By the encouragement of his parents he began to build up his own treasure chest of homoeopathic remedies and too, to find in the early days the need to value and to learn the undoubted skills of the surgeon. In his early days he was not able to work with those who were interested in his alternative medicine ideas but the skill of the surgeon remains common to all theories and while medication can be used according to the operator's knowledge and convictions, the skill on the surgery table is still common to all in human and animal problems.

It is hoped that Peter's acquired knowledge has given some impetus to the readers, that they too will pursue diligently the healing powers of drugs presented in the harmless form of Homoeopathy.

WHERE TO OBTAIN HOMOEOPATHIC REMEDIES

Ainsworth's Homoeopathic Pharmacy, 38 New Cavendish Street, London, W1M 7LH

The Galen Pharmacy, 1 South Terrace, South Street, Dorchester, Dorset

E. Gould & Son Ltd, 14 Crowndale Road, London, NW1 1TT

A. Nelson & Co. Ltd, 5 Endeavour Way, Wimbledon, London, SW19 9UH

Weleda (UK) Ltd, Heanor Road, Ilkeston, Derbyshire

The above all have a good postal service

For a list of homoeopathic doctors or veterinary surgeons in your area, plus a pack of homoeopathic literature, send an A4 (foolscap) stamped and addressed envelope to;
    The British Homoeopathic Association,
    27a Devonshire Street, London, W1

INDEX